Disney Cinderella
The Summer House

THIS HEAT IS *UNBEARABLE!* WE NEED TO FIND A WAY TO COOL DOWN.

A *SUMMER HOUSE* WOULD COOL YOU DOWN!

PERFECT! I'LL GIVE A PRIZE TO WHOMEVER BUILDS THE *BEST* ONE.

SOON, THE COURT BUILDERS WERE RUNNING AROUND HELPING EVERYONE WITH THEIR SUMMER HOUSE IDEAS.

WHILE CINDERELLA'S EYES WERE CLOSED, HER *FAIRY GODMOTHER* APPEARED AND WAVED HER WAND. IN A FLASH, A BEAUTIFUL BOAT RESTED ON THE WATER.

THERE YOU ARE! NOW ALL YOU NEED ARE SOME DECORATIONS.

OH, THIS IS WONDERFUL! THANK YOU.

WITH THE HELP OF THE BIRDS, CINDERELLA CREATED A BEAUTIFUL WHITE CANOPY TO GIVE THE BOAT SOME SHADE.

JAQ AND GUS SCURRIED AROUND, ADDING SOFT CUSHIONS AND A WONDERFUL FEAST OF CHEESE AND FRUIT.

SOON...

CINDERELLA, THE PRIZE MOST *CERTAINLY* GOES TO YOU!

THE ENTIRE COURT CLIMBED ABOARD THE BEAUTIFUL BOAT AND SAILED DOWN THE RIVER...

A TOAST TO CINDERELLA... WHERE *IS* SHE?

...WELL, MAYBE NOT THE *ENTIRE* COURT.

PEACE AND QUIET AT LAST!

WAS THIS YOUR PLAN THE WHOLE TIME?

THE END!

THE LITTLE MERMAID
The Doll's House

ONE DAY, ARIEL NOTICED THAT HER SISTERS SEEMED BORED . . .

THERE'S NOTHING *FUN* TO DO AT THE PALACE.

WHY DON'T WE GO OUT AND *FIND* SOME FUN, THEN?

SOON . . .

LOOK-- WE FOUND SOMETHING ALREADY!

ARIEL PUT ON A DRESS AND SOME
SPARKLY JEWELRY...

OH,
NICE! LET'S ALL
TRY.

STAYING
AT HOME IS SO
MUCH FUN, DON'T
YOU THINK?

ONCE ARIEL WAS SURE THAT HER
SISTERS WERE HAPPY, SHE SWAM
BACK TO THE SHIPWRECK...

NOW, WHERE WERE
WE? OH RIGHT--I CAN'T
WAIT TO SHOW YOU BOTH
MY COLLECTION...

THE END!

Beauty and the Beast
Butterfly Belle

IT WAS TIME FOR THE ANNUAL CARNIVAL IN BELLE'S VILLAGE! BELLE VISITED HER FATHER FOR THIS SPECIAL OCCASION...

LOOK, PAPA-- THERE'S A CONTEST FOR THE BEST FLOAT THIS YEAR!

WOULDN'T IT BE GREAT TO WIN AND LEAD THE PARADE?

IT WOULD! AND THERE'S ONLY ONE WAY TO DO IT. WHY DON'T *YOU* ENTER THE CONTEST, BELLE?

11

BELLE WAS AMAZED WHEN SHE SPOTTED THE BUTTERFLY THE BEAST HAD FREED...

YOU'RE A LUCKY OMEN, AREN'T YOU?

I'M SO PROUD OF YOU, BELLE. EXCELLENT JOB!

SOON, BACK AT THE CASTLE...

I REALLY WISH YOU COULD HAVE SEEN THE PARADE!

IT LOOKS LIKE OUR LITTLE FRIEND HAS RETURNED--WITH A FEW MORE!

Jasmine
Perfect Parade

IT WAS NEARLY TIME FOR *THE SULTAN'S* CORONATION CELEBRATION AND *JASMINE* WANTED TO DO SOMETHING *EXTRA* SPECIAL THIS YEAR.

WE COULD ARRANGE A CORONATION PARADE THROUGH THE STREETS OF *AGRABAH* . . .

THAT'S A *SUPER* IDEA!

AUDITIONS FOR THE BIG PARADE WERE ORGANIZED RIGHT AWAY. EVERYONE IN AGRABAH WAS INVITED!

FROM THE START, THE AUDITIONS WERE VERY IMPRESSIVE . . .

ANYONE CAN CHARM A SNAKE-- BUT NOT TWO AT ONCE!

A JUGGLING *LION?* YOU'RE IN-- AND YOU CAN BRING YOUR *HUMAN,* TOO!

WE HAVE PLENTY OF DANCERS, BUT NONE OF THEM ARE *ELEPHANTS!*

OUR PARADE WILL BE *UNFORGETTABLE!*

you are cordially invited . . .

THE SULTAN SENT OUT INVITATIONS TO ALL HIS IMPORTANT FRIENDS.

ON THE DAY OF THE PARADE, THE SULTAN WAS VERY EXCITED.

MY GUESTS ARE GOING TO BE AMAZED!

JASMINE BEGAN TO DANCE AT THE FRONT OF THE PARADE. ALL OF THE PERFORMERS AND THEIR ANIMALS FOLLOWED HER.

JASMINE'S DANCING LOOKED LIKE SO MUCH FUN THAT, SOON, EVERYONE JOINED IN!

I KNEW OUR PARADE WOULD BE UNFORGETTABLE!

THE END!

Disney
Sleeping Beauty
The Color Fairies

AURORA WAS WATERING THE FLOWERS IN HER GREENHOUSE WHEN HER *FAIRY GODMOTHERS* ARRIVED WITH A GIFT.

IT'S A SPECIAL PLATE TO DISPLAY IN THE PALACE, DEAR.

OH, THANK YOU! IT'S BEAUTIFUL.

BACK AT THE PALACE...

PHILLIP--LOOK AT WHAT MY AUNTS GAVE ME--

HMM... WHAT'S HAPPENING TO IT?

SOON, THE FOREST LOOKED COLORFUL AND HAPPY AGAIN, AND THE FAIRIES FINALLY UNDERSTOOD THE BEAUTY OF NATURE. TO THANK AURORA FOR HER WISDOM, A FAIRY PLACED A FLOWER IN THE PRINCESS'S HAIR

...BUT IT SLIPPED AND FELL TO THE GROUND.

PRINCE PHILLIP TIED IT IN PLACE WITH THE RIBBON FROM THE PLATE. JUST THEN, THE RIBBON STARTED TO GLOW...

...AND THEY WERE BACK IN THE PALACE.

LOOKS LIKE WE'RE NOW A PART OF THE STORY, TOO!

AND IT LOOKS EVEN NICER THAT WAY!

THE END!

SOON...

MAYBE DADDY WOULD LIKE SOME ICE CREAM!

STEP RIGHT UP! EVERYONE ALWAYS FINDS OUR TREATS... *ENCHANTING.*

KING TRITON STARTED SNEEZING AND COULDN'T STOP...

WHEN *ANDRINA* AND *AQUATA* TRIED THEIR ICE CREAM, THEIR HAIR CHANGED COLOR...

Beauty and the Beast
A Perfect Match

ON THE ANNIVERSARY OF THEIR FIRST MEETING, *BELLE* AND *THE BEAST* BOTH WOKE UP WITH WONDERFUL PARTY IDEAS.

OVER BREAKFAST THEY EXPLAINED THEIR IDEAS TO EACH OTHER...

PINK AND FLUFFY IS JUST NOT MY STYLE, BELLE.

LET'S SEE IF WE CAN PLAN A PARTY USING BOTH IDEAS.

WILL YOU ALL HELP US?